....

clink

I THINK YOU MEANT TO LEAVE THIS HERE.

AND I SLEPT SOUNDLY IN REN'S ARMS FOR THE FIRST TIME IN DAYS...

AND WOKE UP REFRESHED, AS IF I'D BEEN EXORCISED.

I DIDN'T HAVE TO GO TO WORK THAT DAY...

S sssss...

MY UM- BRELLA'S OVER AT REN'S.

IT'S RAIN- ING...

DAMN.

BUT WHEN I REALIZED THEY WERE REALLY BROKEN, I COULDN'T SIT STILL.

I COULDN'T BELIEVE HACHI TOOK MY GLASS TOO...

THE STRAWBERRY GLASSES WERE GONE.

BEHAVE?!

"YOUR LADY'S SO VIOLENT. MAKE HER BEHAVE!"

TAKUMI TOLD ME...

BUT HE'S SO VIOLENT HIMSELF.

crunch

ACTUALLY, BOTH GLASSES GOT BROKEN.

WHAT?!

YOU DON'T USUALLY BREAK TWO ACCIDENTALLY.

I GUESS THEY THOUGHT YOU FREAKED OUT AND BROKE THOSE GLASSES ON PURPOSE.

WHEN HACHIKO SAW WHAT HAPPENED, SHE WAS SHOCKED AND STARTED TO CRY, AND TAKUMI HAD A HARD TIME CALMING HER DOWN.

14

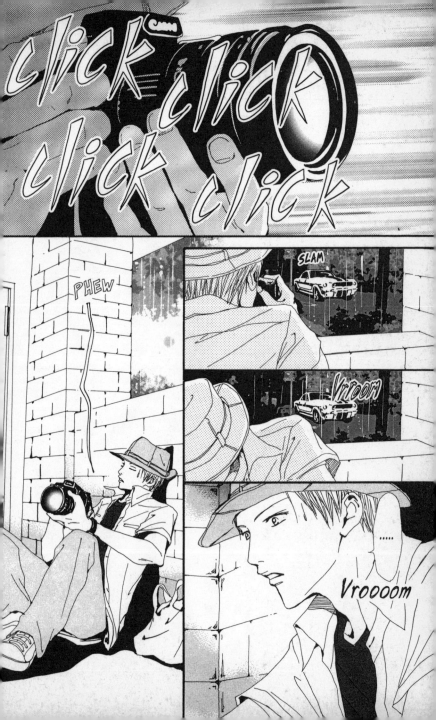

I SURE GOT LUCKY.

I THINK THE RAIN MADE IT HAPPEN.

THE TRIGGER THAT RUINS SOME- ONE'S FATE...

...CAN BE PULLED IN AN INSTANT.

TRIGGER

TRAPNEST

fs —sh

RING

RING

beep

RING

14:40

HELLO, MS. ICHINOSE.

ARE YOU GOING OUT?

COULD YOU CALL ME A CAB?

Ms. Ichinose

SURE THING. WHERE TO?

YEAH!

TO SHIRO-GANE STATION.

UGH

IT HAS TO BE AROUND HERE SOME-WHERE...

I CAN'T FIND IT.

THIS SUCKS!

山医院
白金7丁目
バス停そば
白 金
7 — 14

to-ku
ane 7-chome
Shi...gane

IT'S SUP-POSED TO BE A 20-MINUTE WALK FROM THE STATION, BUT IT SEEMS LIKE I'VE BEEN WALKING FOR AN HOUR.

IF I HAD MONEY FOR AN UMBRELLA, I GUESS I COULD'VE CAUGHT A CAB.

BUT AN UMBRELLA'S CHEAPER.

¥500

I NEED AN UMBRELLA TO GO TO PRACTICE ANYWAY.

Vrrrooom

I'M LOOKING FOR THIS ADDRESS. DO YOU KNOW WHERE THIS IS?

EX-CUSE ME—

Sssssh

I JUST HAVE TO ACT NORMALLY...

...LIKE NOTHING HAPPENED.

...THAT NO MATTER WHAT, THE HERO IS ALWAYS ON THE HEROINE'S SIDE!

BUT I'LL SHOW HER...

'CAUSE SHE THINKS I'M A HERO OF JUSTICE.

HACHI THINKS I'M MAD AND TAKING NOBU'S SIDE, THAT I'M BEING SOME VIGILANTE.

....

th-thump
th-thump
th-thump

SORRY, NOBUO!

23

NANA KOMATSU?

THERE'S NO ONE BY THAT NAME LIVING HERE.

I DON'T BELIEVE IT!

SHE JUST MOVED HERE RECENTLY...

WAIT... IT'S IN TAKUMI'S NAME.

WHAT'S HIS LAST NAME?

IS TAKUMI EVEN HIS REAL NAME?

I'M SORRY, I CAN'T HELP YOU.

302
Ichinose, Takumi
Nana

(Caution) Refuse all requests from any visitor without an appointment. Please tell suspicious people that the room is unoccupied, so they won't return.

TAKUMI FROM TRAPNEST IS LIVING WITH MY FRIEND IN APARTMENT 302!

YOU DON'T HAVE TO LIE ABOUT IT, I ALREADY KNOW!

'CAUSE WE KNOW EACH OTHER!

HOW THE HELL SHOULD I KNOW TAKUMI'S REAL NAME?!

THERE'S NO ONE LIVING HERE BY THAT NAME EITHER.

Pssssh

TAKUMI?! AS IF!

I KNOW THAT STUPID CONCIERGE THINKS I'M A TAKUMI STALKER.

GOD-DAM-MIT!

EVEN REN'S PLACE DOESN'T TREAT PEOPLE LIKE THAT!

HOW COULD SECURITY BE THIS TIGHT?!

THERE'S NO ONE LIVING IN THAT APARTMENT RIGHT NOW.

LEAVE IT TO TAKUMI TO THINK OF THE PERFECT WAY TO ISOLATE HER.

A DRASTIC MEASURE WITH NO WIGGLE ROOM.

HOW YOU CAME TO THINK THAT YOUR MOTHER SHOULDN'T HAVE HAD YOU.

THEN ...

PLEASE TELL ME, SHIN...

...WANT MY CHILD TO THINK LIKE THAT.

I DEFINITELY DO NOT...

BUT EVEN IF THAT HAPPENS ...

AND I THINK MY CHILD WILL BE SUSPICIOUS IF THEY DON'T LOOK LIKE HIM.

...I THINK TAKUMI WILL SUFFER TOO.

BUT IF THE BABY ISN'T REALLY TAKUMI'S ...

...THAT IF WE TRY, WE CAN HAVE A HAPPY FAMILY.

...I STILL WANT TO HAVE HOPE...

MY GOAL IS ALWAYS TO INCREASE BUSINESS... TO SELL MORE COPIES OF OUR MAGAZINE!

WHEN THE TV SHOW BREAKS THEIR LOVE SCANDAL, IT WORKS UP PUBLIC INTEREST, THEN EVERYONE WILL JUMP AT OUR PHOTOS AND STORY!

YOU KNOW IT. ♡

YOU HAVE PHOTOS OF THEM TOGETHER?

OH '''

SSSSHH···

TICKETS

EXCEL SHIROKANE

210

beep

GODDAMMIT.

I WAITED FOR HACHI IN FRONT OF HER BUILDING UNTIL THE SUN WENT DOWN...

NOW I REALLY AM TURNING INTO A STALKER.

BUT I NEVER SAW HER.

I'LL COME BACK TOMORROW WHEN I GET OFF WORK.

IT'S NOT LIKE I'LL NEVER SEE HER AGAIN.

IF I GET HER PHONE NUMBER FROM YASU, I'LL BE ABLE TO SEE HER.

I'LL HAVE A LITTLE TIME BEFORE PRACTICE.

THERE'S ALWAYS TOMORROW.

THE ONLY TIME I GO OUT IS FOR GROCERIES AND MY DOCTOR APPOINT-MENTS.

YOU'RE RIGHT...

HOUSE-WIVES ARE HUNGRY FOR SOMEONE TO TALK TO!

...BUT I'M GLAD WE GOT TO TALK ABOUT THINGS.

I'M SORRY I TALKED YOUR EARS OFF...

....

YOU CAN MAKE NEW FRIENDS, AND IT MIGHT BE FUN.

WHY DON'T YOU TAKE A CLASS OR SOME-THING?

YEAH!

THAT'S A GOOD IDEA! ♥

GOOD THING YOU TOLD ME!

THANKS, MAN!

YOU SHOULDN'T JUST STAY HOME ALL DAY, THINKING ABOUT YOUR BABY. YOU HAVE TO KEEP CONTACT WITH THE OUTSIDE WORLD, TOO.

Her name is Nana Osaki!

...WHEN THE SKY CLEARED AND THE SPOTLIGHT WAS SUDDENLY ON US...

FROM THAT DAY ON...

...NOT ON THE STAGE, BUT IN THE RING.

...WE FOUND OUR-SELVES STAND-ING...

THE CHEERS AND JEERS...

...STILL RING IN MY HEAD...

...LOUD AND ANNOYING.

...WHICH PISSED ME OFF ROYALLY.

THAT'S WHY I WAS THE ONLY ONE WHO MISSED THE BEGINNING OF THE MEDIA CIRCUS...

BACK THEN, I DIDN'T HAVE A TV OR A PHONE IN MY ROOM.

Living with her boyfriend at sixteen, wow.

The lead singer, Nana, was sixteen then, but she moved in with Ren, who lived on his own.

It sure looks like it.

Ren Honjo has a girlfriend

7

Were they lovers from the beginning?

Black Stones was originally a band that Ren started in his hometown.

She apparently bad-mouthed Ren to anyone who'd listen.

When band mates who're also lovers leave the band, it gets ugly. And Nana is known to be hotheaded.

Yes.

The couple apparently broke up at that point...

Ren was scouted by Trapnest right before they made their major label debut and left Black Stones, right?

We have to break for a commercial here.

boo boo

7

THAT'S SO NOT TRUE!

IT DOESN'T MATTER IF IT'S TRUE OR NOT!

OH SHUT UP! YOU CAN'T LISTEN TO THAT CRAP!

AT ANY RATE, WITH THIS SCANDAL, I CAN'T BE AROUND FOR A WHILE...

DON'T WORRY, I'LL PAY CHILD SUPPORT.

IF YOU'RE WORRIED ABOUT BEING ALONE, YOU CAN GO BACK TO YOUR PARENTS' PLACE AND RAISE THE BABY.

SO JUST DO WHATEVER YOU WANT TO DO.

IS YOUR TAKUMI LIKE... TAKUMI FROM TRAPNEST?!

HELLO, NANA?!

I'D LIKE TO ASK YOU ABOUT YOUR RELATIONSHIP WITH MR. REN HONJO.

I CAN UNDERSTAND THEM GOING TO REN'S PLACE, BUT WHY ARE THEY STALKING THE GURU'S PLACE, TOO?!

SHE'S NOT EVEN A CELEBRITY... YET!

SHE SHOULD DEFINITELY SUE THEM!

WHAT ABOUT YASU?!

THEY KEEP SHOWING THE LIVE FOOTAGE FROM THEIR SHOW... IT'S WEIRD.

IT'S A COOL OLD BUILDING, AND WITH THE SURROUNDINGS IN THE SHOT, PEOPLE WILL FIGURE OUT WHERE IT IS.

IT'S NOT LOOKING GOOD. THEY MIGHT HAVE FIGURED OUT THAT NANA HAD A ROOMMATE...

SO NANA...

ISN'T HE A LAWYER?!

DO SOMETHING!

THINK WHAT'D HAPPEN IF THEY FIND OUT ABOUT YOU AND TAKUMI.

I KNOW YOU WANT TO SEE HER, BUT BE LOGICAL.

THE PAPARAZZI MIGHT CORNER YOU.

YOU NEVER KNOW HOW IT'D PLAY OUT IN THE MEDIA, WHAT IT'D DO TO TAKUMI...

YOU BETTER NOT GO OVER THERE.

AND HOW HARD IT MIGHT BE ON YOU AND THE BABY.

YOU SHOULDN'T LET THE MEDIA FIND OUT WHO YOU ARE.

BUT NANA...

PLEASE JUST STAY OUT OF THIS.

DON'T GO.

I'M MORE WORRIED ABOUT YOU.

SHE'S MATURE, AND SHE HAS HER BAND-MATES.

NANA WILL BE OKAY.

KNOCK KNOCK

PLEASE OPEN UP AND LET US INTERVIEW YOU!

LIKE THE TABLOID SEARCH?

SEARCH...

MS. NANA OSAKI?

CHANNEL 7?!

IF A SKANKY RAG LIKE *THAT* FOUND OUT, WHO KNOWS WHAT THEY'RE GOING TO WRITE!

WE SAW THE CHANNEL 7 EXPOSÉ.

GODDAMMIT!

....

IF YOU DON'T TRY TO EXPLAIN YOURSELF TO THE PUBLIC, THINGS WILL JUST GET WORSE AND WORSE.

EX-PLAIN WHAT?!

...THEN WHY DON'T YOU MAKE YOUR OWN FLOWERS BLOOM?

IF YOU'VE GOT THE TIME TO TRAMPLE ON OTHER PEOPLE'S GARDENS...

IDIOT.

NOW THE PRESS WILL HATE HIM.

UH OH.

....

TRAPNES

SLAM

....

Ren Honjo's Girlfriend!

That was live from Ren's girlfriend Nana's apartment building!

Well, that's it for now!

WIDE 8

HE'S SO COOOL! ♡

BUT I DON'T WANNA BE BALD!

NOW I WANNA BE YASU!

I LOVE YOU!

...

I'M SORRY FOR CALLING YOU BALDY, BALDY!

AWW... SO YASU REALLY IS THE COOLEST! ♡

TAKUMI!?

WHAT CAN I DO?

IF THIS IS ABOUT REN HAVING A GIRLFRIEND, WHY DO THEY KEEP TALKING ABOUT BLAST INSTEAD OF US?

BUT IT'S KIND OF LAME, TOO.

IT'S KIND OF COOL.

ALL THE GOSSIP SHOWS ARE DOING THE SAME STORY.

WOW, REN'S REALLY FAMOUS!

.....

Pout

REN'S GIRLFRIEND!

WHETHER IT'S GOOD OR BAD NEWS, I JUST WANNA BE IN IT!

WELL...

OOOH... JEALOUS MUCH, NAOKI?

IT MEANS THE WORLD'S A PEACEFUL PLACE.

....

KNOCK KNOCK

IT'S TOO MUCH PRESSURE!

I HATE YOU!

ALL RIGHT.

OH, MARI!

MORE COFFEE PLEASE. ♡

THIS IS THE WORST THING EVER!

NANA!

I NEVER WANTED TO BECOME A HOUSEHOLD NAME AS REN'S STUPID GIRLFRIEND.

IF YOU TALK TO ME, I'LL WRITE A FOLLOW-UP ARTICLE EXPLAINING YOUR SIDE OF THE STORY.

WHAT DO YOU HAVE TO SAY ABOUT THAT?

RUMOR HAS IT THAT THIS IS ALL A PUBLICITY STUNT.

I'M FINISHED.

KNOCK KNOCK KNOCK

DON'T SAY MY NAME LIKE YOU KNOW ME!

KNOCK KNOCK NANA!

THEY DON'T STOP, DO THEY?

80

I'm GETTING de-PORTED?!

NO, IT'S FOR THE CD COVER AND PROMO PHOTO SHOOT.

WHAT LAW AM I BREAKING NOW? THERE ARE JUST TOO MANY...

AM I A CRIMINAL?!

ORDERS FROM THE AGENCY...

"GET ON THE AFTER-NOON FLIGHT TO THE UK."

WE'RE MOVING IT TO ENGLAND 'CAUSE OF ALL THE SCANDAL BABBLE.

YOU'LL BE THERE A COUPLE WEEKS, SO YOU'LL HAVE SOME TIME FOR A LITTLE R&R.

IF I'M WITH TAKE, IT'LL BE NICE AND QUIET.

I'LL START GETTING READY.

ALL RIGHT.

I'LL DRIVE YOU TO THE AIRPORT.

BUT YOU AND MR. TAKEDA HAVE TO TAKE OFF TODAY.

YOUR BAND MATES AND STAFF WILL LEAVE TOMOR-ROW...

UM... MR. HONJO?

...SHARES THIS GOAL AND RESPONSIBILITY.

MY BAND...

WHAT I HAVE TO PROTECT NOW...

...ISN'T MY OLD FRIENDS OR PAST BANDMATES.

click click

············

THAT'S GOOD.

THERE, I SAID IT. NOW I'M DONE. ♡

?

FLING

TAXI

Reporting live from the pad of the person in question, Nana!

Vroom

Well, that's all, folks!

HEY, HACHI...

NO ONE KNEW WHAT TO THINK!

AND THE NEXT SPECIAL IS "A FEARLESS NANA AND THE MYSTERIOUS MESSAGE TO HER PET DOG!"

AT LEAST THINGS ARE GETTING SIDE-TRACKED...

SHE REALLY IS FEARLESS!

Ah Ha Ha

EVERYONE MUST THINK HACHI'S A DOG!

Ah Ha Ha

Wag Wag

100

WE HAVE NO CHOICE BUT TO MOVE FORWARD WITH THIS, MR. KAWANO.

EVEN IF THEY BLOW UP WITH THIS TABLOID CRAP, IT'S JUST A SET UP.

I DON'T KNOW...

AT THE EMERGENCY MEETING THIS AFTERNOON, THEY'RE GOING TO PUSH TO MAKE A BLAST RECORD AS SOON AS POSSIBLE.

THE PHONES HAVE BEEN RINGING OFF THE HOOK. EVERYONE'S SUDDENLY CHANGED THEIR MINDS. THEY WANT TO GO FOR IT.

WHEN THIS MAGAZINE HITS THE STANDS TOMORROW, NANA WILL GET BASHED EVEN MORE.

Ren Honjo

MATSUO, YOU'VE SEEN GOOD MUSICIANS WHOSE CAREERS WERE DESTROYED BY RELENTLESS SLANDER AND MAJOR LABELS THAT ONLY CARE ABOUT THE BOTTOM LINE.

102

BUT I'M RELIEVED, 'CAUSE NANA SEEMS TOTALLY FINE.

SHE SAW THE GOSSIP SHOW THIS MORNING AND GOT WORRIED AND RAN OVER HERE.

THAT'S MY MISATO!

THAT'S MY NANA!

HOW DID IT GO WITH GAIA?

WEL- COME HOME, YASU!

WHAT ARE YOU DOING HERE?

DON'T YOU HAVE SCHOOL?

I KNEW SHE'D COME AND HELP US OUT.

WELL, THAT WAS AWFULLY CONSIDER- ATE OF YOU.

SHIN E-MAILED ME AND LET ME KNOW.

OH...

SUPER SLEUTH...

BUT HOW DID YOU KNOW WE WERE HERE?

OH, DON'T WORRY ABOUT THAT.

BUT WHAT ABOUT SCHOOL?

I'M AT YOUR SER- VICE.

I'M IN ROOM 712.

WE CAN'T GO ANY- WHERE, SO WE CAN ASK HER TO RUN ERRANDS FOR US.

MISATO'S STAYING HERE FOR A WHILE, TOO.

.....

I JUST HAD LUNCH WITH MR. KAWANO. I'M STUFFED.

IT'S GOOD YOU'RE HERE.

DON'T WORRY. EAT IT.

OH NO, I CAN'T TAKE YOURS.

Yay!

Food!

ALRIGHTY THEN.

THIS IS FROM MR. NISHIMOTO AT GAIA.

YOU CAN EAT MINE.

SO WHO'S THIS NISHIMOTO?

THEN MAKE US SOME TEA!

I JUST FEEL BAD EATING YOUR FOOD.

OH, THANKS SO MUCH.

A FOX, HUH...

Ha Ha

WELL, LOTS OF GUYS CAME BY TO TAKE A PEEK.

HOW CAN I KEEP 'EM STRAIGHT?

HMMM...

HE CAME BY THE STUDIO ONCE.

HE'S THE HEAD OF GAIA'S PRODUCTION DEPARTMENT.

WHAT WAS HE LIKE?

WHO?

HE WAS SLY LIKE A FOX.

OH YEAH...

shine shine

purrrr

IT'S NOT JUST ME TRYING TO BASK IN THAT SUN.

THAT'S WHY NOBU'S ALWAYS SURROUNDED BY PEOPLE.

I saw U on TV! Awesome! You're an overnight sensation! Gimme your autograph! ♡

beep

Nana's beautiful. Introduce us. She can take advantage of me any time!

beep

So who's Hachi? Nana's pet dog?

Ding dong

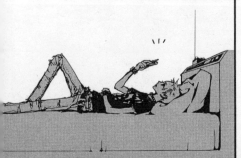

IF YOU CAN'T TAKE IT, GO BACK TO THE TERASHIMA INN.

WHEN I TURNED ON THE TV, I SAW REN SWARMED BY PAPARAZZI ON ALL THE GOSSIP SHOWS.

...MADE ME FEEL KIND OF LEFT BEHIND AND ABANDONED AGAIN.

SEEING REN BEING RUSHED SILENTLY THROUGH THE LOBBY AT NARITA...

I DON'T KNOW WHERE REN'S GOING.

I DON'T KNOW WHAT HE'S DOING.

121

122

BUT THE IDEALS THAT WE PURSUE AND THE REALITY THAT RUSHES TOWARD US KEEP STARING EACH OTHER DOWN.

THEY DON'T GET ALONG.

APPARENTLY, PEOPLE ARE LOCKED INTO A SYSTEM WHERE YOU HAVE TO PAY SOMETHING IN ORDER TO GAIN SOMETHING.

FINALLY, OUR DREAMS ARE COMING TRUE.

THE CYCLE OF WAXING AND WANING IS PURE FATE.

I STARTED TO REALIZE THIS...

knock knock

TIME FOR A DRINK.

I JUST SENT HER A SECRET MESSAGE.

SO NANA...

....

I'VE BEEN GETTING TONS OF E-MAILS ASKING "WHAT'S HACHIKO?" IT'S WORSE THAN PORNO SPAM.

YOU SAID SOMETHING FOR HACHI ON TV, DIDN'T YOU?

I TOLD PEOPLE IT'S YOUR PET DOG.

IT'S ALL RIGHT.

SHE KINDA IS...

THERE, THERE...

SORRY, MAN.

OH ...

WHAT STORY?

IT'S COOL, MAN. THIS IS WHAT I WANT TO BE DOING.

"THE NOBUO DIARIES."

....

I'M JUST LIVING OUT A STORY WHERE I'M TORMENTED BY GIRLS NAMED "NANA."

IF I WEREN'T IN YOUR LIFE, YOU COULD LIVE HAPPILY EVER AFTER IN PEACE.

I'M REALLY SORRY. I KEEP DRAGGING YOU THROUGH DRAMA.

126

SO WHY CAN'T I LET GO?

SHE WAS REALLY HORRIBLE TO ME...

MAYBE YOU DON'T HAVE TO LET GO. THERE'S STILL HOPE.

HOW?!

SLAM

TREATING HER LIKE A DOG AGAIN ...

"MATE WITH HER..."

"OPERATION GET HACHIKO BACK."

WHEN SHE RETURNS TO MY YARD, YOU CAN MATE WITH HER.

....

PLEASE DON'T DO THIS.

WHAT PLAN?!

YOU JUST HAVE TO FOLLOW MY PLAN.

MY DEAR NOBUO...

LET'S JUST DO THE BEST WE CAN TO-GETHER.

...AND WE EXPECT BLAST TO DELIVER.

I PROMISE, GAIA WILL DO EVERY-THING IN ITS POWER TO PROMOTE YOU...

Contract

HEH

NANA.

HEE HEE HEE

?

I'M GETTING A BAD FEELING ABOUT THIS.

GAIA'S GETTING CARRIED AWAY AND JOINED THE MEDIA CIRCUS.

CHECK OUT THE ENHANCEMENTS.

THEY SEEM TO REALLY DIG YOUR LADY.

I'M SURE THESE GUYS LAUNCHED THE WHOLE MEDIA FREAK-OUT.

THE HEAD-LINE'S RIDICU-LOUS, BUT THE CONTENT IS PRETTY CRAZY TOO.

WHY?

WELL, I SURE FELL FOR HER.

PLUNK

SMILE

ARE YOU RETURN-ING THIS?

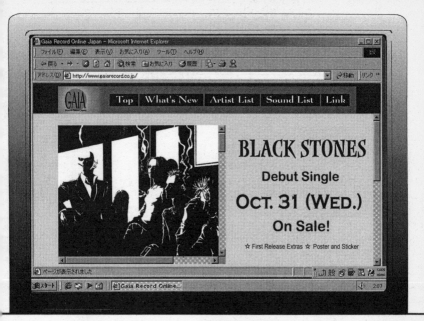

HEY, HACHI...

DEATH TO NANA

I CAN'T BE THE HERO
IN YOUR STORY...

...I CAN'T DO IT ANYMORE.

LOVE
TO NANA♡

...THE FATAL FLAW IN MY PLAN.

I DIDN'T HAVE THE TIME OR ENERGY TO REALIZE...

EVERY DAY WAS JAM-PACKED WITH BAND STUFF. I HARDLY HAD TIME TO SLEEP.

REN...

JUST TRY TO FORGET LADIES LIKE THAT.

CALM DOWN!

REN!

BUT I WANT THE SALTY MISO SOUP THAT *NANA* MAKES!

REN, I THINK NANA'S BAD NEWS LIKE THEY SAY, AND SHE'S TAKING ADVANTAGE OF YOU.

THIS IS A GOOD TIME TO TALK...

LADIES LIKE THAT ?!

IT'S NOT FAIR TAKUMI GOT TO GO HOME FIRST.

I WANT TO GO BACK TO JAPAN NOW.

WHATEVER.

TAKE...

IF SHE REALLY LOVED YOU, SHE WOULDN'T USE SO MUCH SALT WHEN SHE COOKS.

TAKUMI'S GOING HOME BEFORE US?

WHAT ?!

AND TAKUMI HAS HIS REASONS.

YOU STILL HAVE PHOTO SHOOTS.

SORRY.

147

WHY DIDN'T HE TELL US?!

WHAT THE HELL?!

HE SUCKS, MAN.

I THINK HE'S ALREADY BACK IN JAPAN.

HE ALREADY LEFT YESTERDAY.

BY HIMSELF.

BUT HE'S COMING IN LATE AT NIGHT, SO HE'S JUST BEING CONSIDERATE.

AT THE HOTEL, HE'LL HAVE TO WORRY ABOUT HIS PRIVACY.

IF MR. ICHINOSE IS COMING OVER TO MEET US TOMORROW, HE CAN JUST STAY HERE.

MOM?

HE'S PRACTICALLY FAMILY NOW.

HE DOESN'T HAVE TO WORRY ABOUT THAT.

I'M GOING TO GO CHECK IN AT THE HOTEL.

150

THE BEST SHE CAN?

BUT I HEARD THROUGH A MUTUAL FRIEND THAT SHE'S DOING WELL, THE BEST SHE CAN.

AND I HAVEN'T HEARD FROM HER.

NOT REALLY.

SO I CAN'T REALLY CALL OR E-MAIL HER.

I GUESS SHE BROKE HER CELL PHONE...

SHE'S A TOUGH ONE.

THAT'S NANA FOR YOU.

THAT'S TOO BAD...

OH...

I WAS FRANTIC...

WAS IT JEALOUSY?

REIRA...

I HONESTLY DIDN'T WANT TO HEAR ABOUT TAKUMI OR HER BABY.

AND DIDN'T EVEN TRY TO ASK HACHI HOW SHE WAS DOING.

...TO SHOW HACHI MY SINGING, PERFORMING SELF.

YOU DIDN'T EAT ANY OF YOUR BREAKFAST.

I'M ALL RIGHT.

ARE YOU FEELING OKAY?

......

click

WHAT?

DO YOU THINK TAKUMI HOOKED UP WITH STELLA? ♡

HEY, MARI...

I DON'T KNOW...

HE CHANGED HIS SCHEDULE FOR HIS FIANCÉE.

BUT TAKUMI WAS SO BUSY HERE, I DON'T THINK HE HAD TIME FOR ANY PLAY.

REALLY?

OH...

WELL, THAT MIGHT BE GOOD FOR HIS FIANCÉE, BUT STELLA WAS TAKUMI'S GIRLFRIEND LONG BEFORE THAT.

THAT'S NOT COOL.

WHAT?!

I FEEL KIND OF SORRY FOR STELLA.

I BET SHE WAS SECRETLY DREAMING OF MARRYING TAKUMI SOMEDAY...

Incoming Mail

Subject

It's Shin

Reira, how're you doing? Have you been able to relax a little in London?

We're way off in the mountains up north, so we can hunker down to write and record our new album.

Recording's been good, but we've been put on an exercise regimen that's kind of grueling. (But seeing Yasu in workout clothes makes it all worthwhile!) I don't really get why they're making us do all this.

But after being on a regular schedule for five days, I feel good and think I've even grown a little taller.

But maybe it's just my imagination!

THEN SHE COULD HAVE COOKED FOR US.

MISATO SHOULD HAVE COME WITH US.

WHY'S EVERYTHING YOU MAKE SO SALTY?

YOU'RE THE ONE WHO ASKED FOR MISO SOUP...

...SO SHUT UP AND EAT!

WE CAN'T MAKE HER DO THAT.

SHE'S RESPONSIBLE, RELIABLE, AND CONSIDERATE.

THAT'S A GREAT IDEA! ♡

MISATO SHOULD JUST QUIT SCHOOL AND BE OUR MANAGER.

I WOULD MUCH RATHER HAVE A CUTE GIRL AS OUR MANAGER.

YEAH ...

156

You might not know cause you're overseas, Reira...

...but the gossip rags have gotten even more insane. They're even gossiping about Yasu now!

Just like they did with Nana, they're dredging up every bit of his past. They're making him out to be a total thug, based on his looks. (But you have to see him in his P.E. uniform!)

I don't know whether they know or not...

...but they haven't reported that you and Yasu used to go out.

So you don't have to worry about anything...yet.

HEY REN—

DID NAOKI TELL YOU ABOUT YASU?

SEARCH JUST WROTE SOME JUICY EXPOSÉ ABOUT HIM.

NO, WHAT HAPPENED TO THE BALDY?

EXPOSÉ ABOUT WHAT?

HE SAW IT BEING TALKED ABOUT ON THE NET.

AND ABOUT HIM PUNCHING A SEARCH REPORTER WHO WAS HARASSING NANA, THEN GETTING QUESTIONED BY THE COPS.

STUFF...

BUT OF COURSE IT'S NOT TRUE.

....

LIES, LIES, LIES.

SO NOW ALL THE OTHER MAGAZINES...

...ARE SAYING THAT NANA'S ACTUALLY GOING OUT WITH YASU, AND THINGS ARE HEATING UP.

THEY ALSO WROTE THAT YASU DIDN'T PASS THE BAR SO HE ISN'T REALLY A LAWYER.

ISN'T THAT MEAN?

I WAS WONDERING ABOUT THAT RUMOR, TOO.

THANKS, MARI. ♡

OH.

UM... REIRA?

THAT SUCKS.

WHAT'S THE JUDICIAL RESEARCH AND TRAINING INSTI- TUTE?

WHAT?

....

?

LIKE WHAT IF MR. TAKAGI ISN'T REALLY ENROLLED IN THE JUDICIAL RESEARCH AND TRAINING INSTITUTE?

AFTER YOU PASS THE BAR EXAM, YOU HAVE TO ATTEND THE JUDICIAL RESEARCH AND TRAINING INSTITUTE FOR A YEAR AND A HALF IN ORDER TO BECOME A LAWYER.

YOU KNOW, LIKE AN APPREN- TICE.

?

IT'S LIKE A LEGAL INTERN- SHIP.

HOW COOL.

MARI, YOU KNOW EVERYTHING! ♡

REALLY?

♪

REALLY ?!

OH, AND YOU DO?!

SHEESH.

JUST 'CAUSE YOU DON'T KNOW ANY- THING, REIRA.

...I MAJORED IN LAW.

WELL, I DON'T THINK IT'S NECESSARILY COMMON KNOWLEDGE, BUT...

I don't wear diapers!

LIKE CHANGING DIAPERS.

WHADDYA MEAN, BABY-SITTING?!

HEY, DON'T WORRY ABOUT ME...

punch punch

YOU DON'T WEAR THOSE GLASSES FOR NOTHING!

THAT'S AMAZING.

AND MY GLASSES ARE FAKE!

OH, IT'S REALLY NO BIG DEAL.

SO THEN WHY'RE YOU BABY-SITTING REIRA?

WHY AM I IN A BAND WITH GUYS WHO HIT ON EVERY GIRL THEY SEE?!

YOU PIGS!

LET'S CHAT MORE LATER.

NO, I WANT TO KNOW MORE ABOUT YOU, MARI.

......

IT'S BEEN MORE THAN A YEAR AND A HALF SINCE HE GRADUATED FROM COLLEGE, SO MAYBE HE'S ALREADY A LAWYER.

SO THEN ISN'T HE IN THAT TRAINING RIGHT NOW?

SO THAT'S WHY YASU CALLS HIMSELF AN APPRENTICE.

IF HE'S DOING THE BAND THIS SERIOUSLY, I DON'T SEE HOW HE COULD DO BOTH AT THE SAME TIME.

WELL...

WHEN YOU GO INTO TRAINING, YOU HAVE TO GO TO THE TRAINING INSTITUTE YOU'RE ASSIGNED TO. YOU CAN'T JUST GO WHEREVER YOU WANT FOR THE ACTUAL INTERNSHIP EITHER.

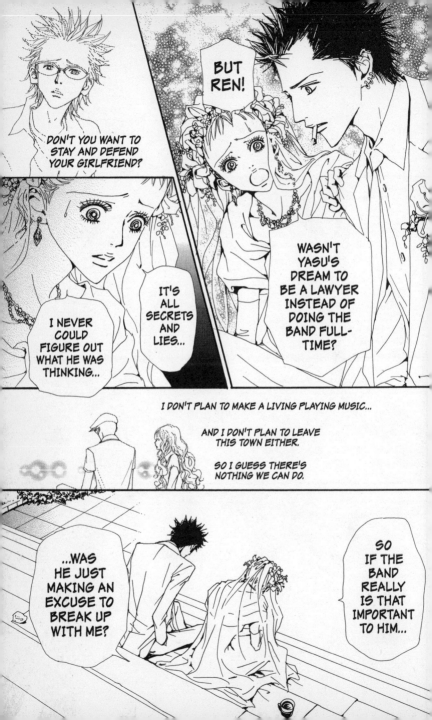

If you tell me you're lonely, Reira...

I'll fly to London right now.
Or anywhere else in the world.

If that'll warm your heart and body just a little, I'm there.

It's not that I'm trying to be nice or anything.

But it's just that I'm feeling like...

...there's nothing else important to me right now.

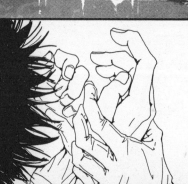

So I don't know what tomorrow will bring.

I'm sorry I've been so self-centered.

Ding dong

click

Creak

174

THEN THIS IS FOR LI'L SACHI. ♡

HERE.

SACHIKO ICHI-NOSE.

WHAT A TONGUE-TWISTER.

BUT IT DOESN'T REALLY SOUND RIGHT.

THANK YOU, DADDY! ♡

↑ Like a cocktail waitress.

E E K! ♡

THEY'RE SO CUTE!

AND SO MANY! ♡

Reira...

I bought a laptop, as you can see...

YOU'RE THE ONE WHO NAMED HER THAT!

PLEASE! SHE WON'T HAVE AN EVIL NAME LIKE THAT!

Cause I wanted to use up all the money you gave me.

But I didn't wanna spend it just on myself.

I bought the acoustic guitar for the same reason.

I can't get romantic enough to sing if my voice can't reach you.

So I'll be e-mailing you when I can.

Please write back if you feel like it.

Let's talk soon.

The weather's nice today, so there'll be lots of stars out tonight.

Shinichi Okazaki

FLICK

HEY,
FAKE
LAWYER...
♡

WHAT
ARE YOU
DOING,
HIDING
IN THE
DARK?

IT'S NOT LIKE WE'RE ONE ANY- MORE, LIKE BEFORE.

EVEN WHEN I'M WITH REN, I'M LONELY INSIDE.

...IT FEELS LIKE MY BOND WITH *YOU* HAS GOTTEN STRONGER THAN MY BOND WITH REN.

...IN THE TWO AND A HALF YEARS AFTER REN AND I FIRST BROKE UP...

MY FEELINGS FOR REN HAVEN'T CHANGED AT ALL.

I DON'T KNOW WHY.

MAI.

YUI.

AKANE.

SUMIRE.

A ONE-KANJI NAME WOULD BE GOOD.

SINCE YOUR LAST NAME IS THREE KANJI, IT WOULD LOOK NICE IN WRITING

SACHI-KO'S FINE.

LIKE YOUR NAME, TAKUMI.

SO IT'S GONNA BE SACHI-KO. ♡

BUT I'M STARTING TO LIKE IT.

HELP ME THINK OF A GOOD NAME!

NO WAY!

HEY, HACHI...

THE SKY IS SPRINKLED WITH STARS...

...AND TONIGHT, THE SKY IS JUST SO BRIGHT.

EVEN NOW...
...WHEN I SEE SOMETHING SPARKLING...

...IT REMINDS ME OF REN.

Woo! But the English version is correct! Thanks Mari!

188

189

A COMPILATION BOOK OF THE READERS' ILLUSTRATIONS?

OH...

......

THAT'S AWESOME.

I HOPE THEY PICK GOOD PICTURES OF ME. I WANT TO LOOK HOT LIKE NANA!

WITH COOL CLOTHES! ♡

CHEERS!

THEY'RE GOING TO PUBLISH A "NANA" ILLUSTRATION COLLECTION!

WHAT'S THAT?

HUH?

clink

BLACK STONES

ARIELLE GARCIA
Metairie

ROCIO TREJO
Skokie

ANA BARAJAS
Anthony

a thr is born

NHHA

JENNIFER HARBOTTLE
Oswego

THE BLACK STONES

LAUREN CHAIKIN
South Euclid

WELL, IT'S NOT REALLY A PHOTO BOOK.

LIKE A PHOTO BOOK?

AN ILLUSTRATION COLLECTION OF A MANGA USUALLY HAS COLOR PAGES FROM THE MAIN STORY.

NO SHIN, IT'S NOT THAT.

NO MATTER HOW MUCH WE STRUGGLE, WE CAN NEVER BECOME REAL HUMANS.

BECAUSE WE ARE JUST RESIDENTS OF A FICTIONAL WORLD, WE CAN ONLY LIVE ON PAPER.

ACTUALLY, YOU *ARE* A KID, SHIN!

PUT DOWN THAT DRINK!

I'M NOT JUST SOME DUMB KID LIVING IN A FANTASY WORLD.

DON'T MESS WITH ME, JUNKO.

LIKE AN EMERGENCY STAIRWELL?

WE'RE FREE! WE CAN GO BACK TO THE SEVENTH FLOOR!

BUT WHY IS THERE A DOOR NOT CONNECTED TO ANYTHING ELSE IN THE MIDDLE OF NOWHERE?

MAYBE IT'S A TRAP!

IF THIS MANGA GOES ON UNTIL VOL. 77, I DON'T THINK THEY'LL LET US OUT THAT EASY!

HEY, NANA...

THERE'S A DOOR HERE.

ISN'T THIS AN EMERGENCY EXIT SIGN?

WHERE DOES IT LEAD TO?

WHAT?

191

THERE'S NO WAY I'M HANGING AROUND THAT LONG!

BAM

NANA!

AND I WISH I COULD HAVE HOOKED UP WITH MR. ASANO AGAIN, AND MARRIED HIM IN THE MAIN STORY! ♡

IT'S TOO BAD WE DIDN'T GET TO MEET GEORGE...

THE SERIES MUST HAVE BEEN CANCELLED, AND THE MANGAKA HAD TO END THE STORY QUICK.

SEE... IT'S JUST A STAIR-CASE.

OH... PHEW!

EVEN IF IT'S SOME WEIRD HOCUS POCUS, WE SUR-VIVED, WHICH IS ALL RIGHT BY ME.

YEAH! ♡

ALL RIGHT, LET'S JUST GET BACK TO THE SEVENTH FLOOR AND THINK GOOD THOUGHTS.

HEY, NANA...

SLIP

AAAH H H #

IF I'D BEEN MORE MATURE BACK THEN...

...AND REALIZED HOW DEEP THIS WORLD WAS...

...WOULD MY FUTURE HAVE TURNED OUT ANY DIFFERENT?

SEND US YOURS, TOO! ♡

HERE'S THE AD-DRESS!

MAYBE I SHOULD SEND IN MY POR-TRAIT!

Nana
c/o Shojo Beat
VIZ Media
PO Box 77010
San Francisco,
CA 94133

I LIKE THIS WAY BETTER THAN THE MAIN STORY.

THIS IS CRAZIER AND LESS DEPRESS-ING.

HMMM.... NANA HAS WEIRD BONUS PAGES LIKE THIS?

NANA AND HACHI'S SURVIVAL ADVENTURE CONTINUES!
WE'LL BE OPEN IN VOL. II, TOO!

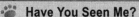

Kagen no Tsuki is going to be made into a movie!

Live-action cinema with a gorgeous cast!
Details in the next volume! Don't miss it!

Fall 2004: First-run showings at Shochiku theaters nationwide.

(Director/Script) Ken Nikai

Natural disasters can't be prevented, but man-made disasters don't have to occur. That's what I think. I didn't end up writing real world events into the *Nana* story, cause there are people who would have been deeply affected by my retelling. I wouldn't be able to keep it ambiguous enough, and I didn't want to just brush over the issue irresponsibly. I hope you all understand. –Ai Yazawa

Ai Yazawa is the creator of many popular manga titles, including *Tenshi Nanka Janai* (I'm No Angel) and *Gokinjo Monogatari* (Neighborhood Story). Another series, *Kagen no Tsuki* (Last Quarter), was made into a live-action movie and released in late 2004. American readers were introduced to Yazawa's stylish and sexy storytelling in 2002 when her title *Paradise Kiss* was translated into English.

Nana has become the all-time best-selling shojo title from Japanese publishing giant Shueisha, and the series even garnered a Shogakukan Manga Award in the girls category in 2003. A live-action *Nana* movie was released in Japan in 2006.

NANA
VOL. 10

The Shojo Beat Manga Edition

STORY AND ART BY AI YAZAWA

English Adaptation/Allison Wolfe
Translation/Tomo Kimura
Touch-up Art & Lettering/Sabrina Heep
Cover Design/Courtney Utt
Interior Design/Julie Behn
Editor/Pancha Diaz

Editor in Chief, Books/Alvin Lu
Editor in Chief, Magazines/Marc Weidenbaum
VP of Publishing Licensing/Rika Inouye
VP of Sales/Gonzalo Ferreyra
Sr. VP of Marketing/Liza Coppola
Publisher/Hyoe Narita

Printed in Canada

Published by VIZ Media, LLC
P.O. Box 77010
San Francisco, CA 94107

Shojo Beat Manga Edition
10 9 8 7 6 5 4 3 2 1
First printing, May 2008